THE VETERINARY CAREGIVER'S BOOK OF QUOTES

*A Collection of Meditations,
Short Tails, and Puppy Kisses*

Katherine Dobbs, RVT, CVPM, PHR

AAHA
press

The Veterinary Caregiver's Book of Quotes
Copyright © 2010 Katherine Dobbs

press

American Animal Hospital Association Press
12575 West Bayaud Avenue
Lakewood, Colorado 80228
800/252-2242 or 303/986-2800
press.AAHAnet.org

ISBN 978-1-58326-117-0

Library of Congress Cataloging-in-Publication Data

Dobbs, Katherine.
 The veterinary caregiver's book of quotes : a collection of meditations, short tails, and puppy kisses / Katherine Dobbs.
    p. ; cm.
  ISBN 978-1-58326-117-0 (pbk. : alk. paper)
  1. Veterinary medicine—Quotations, maxims, etc. 2. Animal health technicians—Quotations, maxims, etc. I. Title.
  [DNLM: 1. Veterinary Medicine. 2. Animal Technicians—psychology. 3. Professional Practice. SF 758 D632v 2009]
  SF758.D63 2009
  636.089—dc22
                          2009047632

Book design: Erin Johnson
Cover images: iStockphoto.com

10   11   12   /   1   2   3   4   5   6   7   8   9   10

For Val,
a superb technician
and an even better friend

ACKNOWLEDGMENTS

This book would not have been possible without you, the veterinary professional. Whether you are the veterinary technician healing pets, the front office team members helping people, or the practice manager who is steering the course, you are all an inspiration.

Thanks also to Laurel Lagoni, MS, for her insightful suggestions for keeping the guidance in these pages as constructive as possible.

PREFACE

My journey to this book began when I was invited to write *101 Veterinary Technician Questions Answered* (AAHA Press, 2009). Technicians across the country were asked to send us descriptions of their top three most challenging problems. These responses came to me, and as I read through the problems identified by veterinary technicians, I literally went from laughing to crying, experiencing all the emotions of my colleagues in the veterinary profession: frustration at the difficult working conditions, joy in helping the pets they love, sadness for the ones they couldn't help, and pride in the work they do so well. One of the statements stood out: "Why is there no help for those of us suffering from burnout?" At that moment I felt compelled not only to answer the 101 questions about our work, but to do something more.

We rephrased the top challenging problems into 101 questions and sent out a second survey to obtain answers from other veterinary technicians. When the responses to our second survey came pouring in, it was clear to me that our best support is one another, those who do the same work we do. If we would only listen to one another, we would find all the inspiration and comfort we need to get through our worst days. So I proposed a different kind of book. I wanted to take a sample of inspirational quotes from the responses we received to the survey for *101 Veterinary Technician Questions Answered* and essentially give those wonderful, heartfelt words back to the profession as inspiration. Some of the technicians quoted in this book were also instrumental in creating *101 Veterinary Technician Questions Answered*; here are their comments in their own words.

I pride myself on being a credentialed technician, but when I began in this profession, I had no credentials for administering patient care. By definition, I was a veterinary assistant. I simply wanted to be around the profession and find my place in it. I joined a small, one-veterinarian practice, where I got experience doing it all, from answering phones to bathing patients, from filling out vaccine reminder cards to assisting in surgery. Many years later I obtained a position as a client service technician at a referral practice. When I visited the first veterinarian I had worked with, I explained to her that this new position was a liaison between the client and the practice. She responded, "That makes sense; you were always the best front person I ever had." At first I wasn't sure how to take this comment, after I had spent so many years obtaining my technician's credentials. Yet as I watched the front office team at the referral practice, I realized it was a wonderful compliment, because the front office is one of the most difficult places to be on the veterinary team. In this book we hear from a variety of front office team members as they describe their important roles in the practice. They return day after day to do the work they love, helping pets and their families. It is truly inspiring.

From "front person" to credentialed technician, I pursued my career in veterinary medicine. As the years went by, I came to respect the people who make veterinary medicine such a wonderful profession. I wanted to find ways to make it better for us all, so my career turned to practice management. No one could have prepared me for the new set of challenges I would face. We hear about some of these in the quotes in this book, from those who lead their teams. Managers must walk a fine line to earn respect from their team members while maintaining the proper amount of emotional distance. It is often a lonely position, because they cannot share certain things with the team that reports to them, and yet they may not want to admit their frustration or doubt to the practice owner. They juggle all sorts of duties and difficulties, with very little soothing interaction with the pets we all came into this profession to help. It takes a special set of qualities to lead the team.

The veterinary profession includes people with many types of education, credentials, and position titles. In this book, position titles are spelled out when applicable, but following is a key to the recognized credentials in veterinary medicine and the educational achievements listed with the quotes:

AS	Associate of Science
AAS	Associate of Applied Science
BA	Bachelor of Arts
BS	Bachelor of Science

BSBA	Bachelor of Science in Business Administration
BIS	Bachelor of Interdisciplinary Studies
CVA	Certified Veterinary Assistant
CVPM	Certified Veterinary Practice Manager
CVT	Certified Veterinary Technician
DVM	Doctor of Veterinary Medicine
LMSW	Licensed Master Social Worker
LVT	Licensed Veterinary Technician
MS	Master of Science
MM	Master of Management
RVT	Registered Veterinary Technician
VTS	Veterinary Technician Specialist

Specialties
DENTISTRY

ECC	Emergency Critical Care
SAIM	Small Animal Internal Medicine

Each quote is followed by my response to the points raised.

It is amazing to me that despite the difficulties, regardless of the conditions, no matter the obstacles, we each believe so strongly in our purpose. A collective pride is exhibited in these quotes, as well as a strength that is both admirable and inspiring. We need only to hang on to that purpose, and each other, to remain inspired to do the work of healing pets and helping people.

THE
VETERINARY
CAREGIVER'S
QUOTES
BOOK
OF

Come in with a good attitude and realize
that your life is what you make it.

ALICIA LEE
Lakeland, Florida

This is a great way to start your day, and a great way to begin your journey through this book. These are the words of your colleagues, other veterinary professionals, who know what it's like to have the challenging job that you have as a technician, assistant, receptionist, or manager, and they have made the best of sometimes difficult situations. In life, there is no better way to start each morning than to look in the mirror and realize that you are ultimately in control of your own life, then go into work with the right kind of mind-set to make the day a good one, for you and your teammates.

"

Be sincerely loyal and committed to your practice and mission. Live and work as guided by the mission. Understand your boss's perspective, and if you don't, ask questions so that you can understand and support that perspective. Know your boss's weaknesses and offer to do those tasks for him or her so that the practice manager and owner form a complete team that complements one another. Provide solutions to problems, not just problems.

JODI PERETTI
Butte, Montana

As a team leader, there is nothing more important than modeling the mission of the practice. To fulfill a leadership role and support the mission, you must understand the practice owner's vision for the future of the business. You may need to ask for this insight; sometimes it is expressed in a way that helps you understand your role. Sometimes it may seem as if you and the practice owner are on opposite sides and have quite different views. That's okay; you may provide excellent balance for each other. You each bring your own strengths and opportunities to grow to the practice. You can help each other reach your personal potential, and together, you can help the practice reach its potential.

I feel like the majority of veterinarians who enter the field and are new to practices understand the importance and active role technicians play in practice. The "old school" veterinarians are probably the hardest to gain respect from, as they are used to doing it all on their own. Technicians need to be patient and let the veterinarians see for themselves how we can make a difference.

DIANE BECKER, RVT
Charlotte, North Carolina

Different generations do perceive veterinary technology, and the role of veterinary technicians in the practice, in different ways. New graduates from veterinary school are now exposed to credentialed technicians during their initial training in veterinary school, so they know the importance of technicians from early on. Those veterinarians who have been working in a practice on their own will be more reluctant to hand over the reins to veterinary technicians, who represent what is still a rather young profession. These veterinarians will need a little more time to recognize how a veterinary technician can help them and their practice. Be patient and demonstrate the extent of your contributions. Share what you have learned in school and through your experience. Ask the veterinarian for the opportunity to demonstrate how valuable you can be to the practice, first under supervision, and then more on your own as he or she grows to trust you. A great overall look at the veterinary technology profession is Dennis M. McCurnin and Joanna M. Bassert's *Clinical Textbook for Veterinary Technicians* (Elsevier/Saunders, 2006). Encourage your boss or practice owner to glance through this book's table of contents. Pull out topics to provide continuing education to other members of the practice, such as assistants and front office team members. This is a great way to demonstrate the scope of the education involved in veterinary technology. Time and trust will take you far!

I make a difference in the practice not only through
my skills and knowledge, but by treating each
patient, client, coworker, and boss with respect
and by caring for each patient as if he or she were
all I had to take care of at that moment.

JENNIFER A. COX

We bring not only special skills and specific knowledge to our practice and the profession, but also our caring and helpful attitude. Care for patients as if they were your own pets, and deal with clients as if they were your own family, and you will rarely go wrong. Treat them all with respect, and you will be respected in turn. Give them your best, and you can be proud of yourself each day when you clock out at the end of your shift. You *do* make a difference!

Volunteer first before entering veterinary medicine, if at all possible. Make sure to see everything—not just the cute, healthy puppies and kittens. There are days when there is a lot more bad than good, and you have to make it to the next good day to survive. The Parvo puppies are the most heartbreaking to me. They are so young and so vulnerable, and many won't survive. They need so much love and attention but are isolated from other animals and have limited access to people as well. The worst part is, most of them could have been spared the disease with a cheap vaccine.

Elise M. Atkinson, BA, CVT
Lakewood, Colorado

Some of us knew what we were getting into, because we had been exposed to some type of animal care before starting our careers in veterinary medicine. For those who are entering the field now, it is helpful to see the difficult aspects of veterinary medicine, to be prepared for the ups and downs. The care we provide takes many shapes. It is healing the sick, but it is also preventing disease and sickness in healthy animals. For every one animal that we treat for illness, we save many more by providing wellness visits and preventive medications and immunizations. The sick ones may stand out more in our memory, but we are truly saving hundreds of pets every year!

I provide healthcare advice to clients while convincing them of my ability and authority to do so by prefacing the advice with a quick overview of my background and position in the clinic. I believe educating clients and the public on the abilities and professionalism of technicians is very important.

Kim M. Novick, CVT

Whatever our position in the practice, we are often called upon to be the voice of the doctor, perhaps the bearer of bad news or the one who must pass along advice from the doctor to the client. Clients must be able to trust that we are speaking in the best interests of their pets, and we need the confidence to portray ourselves as knowledgeable. A technician may begin by mentioning his or her education, or an assistant may relay his or her years of experience. A front office team member may begin by relating the advice to a situation he or she has seen firsthand. This helps clients take care of their pets, of course, but it also helps to elaborate on each person's important position on the team. The more the general public understands about our credentials and qualifications, the more they will trust everyone on the team.

I enjoy working the front office because I feel that there is so much more to veterinary care than just the medicine involved. The human-pet bond runs very deep, and it needs to be respected. Being able to help the moms and dads whom we see while they are here with their "furrkids" is very important to me. I love working with the clients. It's fulfilling, challenging, and very humbling at times. Working in the back is very interesting and has its own appeal, but being able to calm a concerned parent or see the smile as they leave with their now-healthy pet is why I love coming to work. I have learned more about myself and about people in general in this position than in any other role I have had in my past.

ANDREA TUCKER, CLIENT CARE PROFESSIONAL
Colorado Springs, Colorado

There is so much more to the veterinary profession than just medicine. There is satisfaction in knowing we are helping animals and the families who love them. All of us in the veterinary profession see pet owners at their best and at their worst. Nowhere is this truer than at the front desk. The front desk team members often see the story unfold, from the beginning when a client enters the practice to the end when he or she leaves with the pet. This can be very rewarding. These visits are made by all sorts of people caring for their pets. By being exposed to various sides of people, we learn more about ourselves as human beings and pet owners.

"

I believe I was hired to perform the tasks that define a practice manager but have numerous other tasks that fall on my desk. I prioritize my duties as a practice manager and complete them accordingly. I delegate tasks to others when applicable. As we are a fairly new and expanding practice, so many times there is not the staff available to delegate to, and as we grow, an assistant is on the list of potential hires. Until then, I work many hours over forty a week . . . after all, I'm salary.

Joseph DeDeo
Latham, New York

The ability to multitask is a prerequisite for everyone on the veterinary healthcare team, including the practice manager. We are all required to do tasks not necessarily defined by our job descriptions. Yet being good at delegating can also be an asset to a manager, and being willing to and capable of taking on a delegated task is one way to get noticed by the management team. When you're ready to make your next career move, your ability to delegate to others or to take on delegated tasks will be one of many aspects considered. Often a practice manager does not have an administrative assistant, so help from other members of the team can be imperative to the success of the manager, the team member, and the entire practice. Yes, we are all asked to put in more hours to make the practice successful, and only some of us qualify for overtime pay!

"

Greet clients by name (if possible) with a smile.
Try to follow through and address their concerns
before they get a chance to object. Treat them and
their pets the way you would want a family member
to be treated, even though it can be really difficult!
By following these suggestions, I'm often who the
difficult clients ask for over and over again. I have
learned over the years to treat it as a compliment.

LAUREN BLUE, BS
Greensboro, North Carolina

Perhaps you're the one who is called on when the difficult or demanding client comes through the door. Lauren sees this as a compliment, which is a wonderful outlook. It takes a very special person to handle difficult interactions and stressful situations. When you're the one who is best at doing this, you possess a special trait, and others recognize this. The empathy that Lauren refers to is important: how would you be feeling if your pet were having the crisis or enduring the illness? If you can put yourself in another person's place and react from that point of view, these challenging moments will turn out better for everyone involved.

Respect is developed first through accurate understanding of the tasks the law permits each member of the veterinary healthcare team. The technician and doctor each bring different skill sets that complement the practice of quality medical care. The doctor needs to utilize the technician to the fullest extent allowable by law and to make clear to all staff that only credentialed technicians will perform those tasks limited to credentialed technicians. In return, the technician needs to learn the doctor's preferences for treatment, surgery, client relations, etc., and provide support, reinforcing the message of the doctor to all staff. Both technician and doctor must commit to remaining current in their field and to teaching each other.

BONNIE LOGHRY, RVT
Marysville, California

As a technician, there is a lot to learn from the veterinarian. It is also satisfying when the veterinarian realizes he or she has something to learn from a technician. Each brings a certain skill set and knowledge base into the practice. It is also important that they both understand their state's practice laws and the legal boundaries of the positions on the support team. Practice owners who follow these legal guidelines will be more respected by veterinary technicians.

In my role as a practice manager, I enjoyed working with the clients as well as the pets. It was especially rewarding to successfully repair a damaged relationship and turn an unhappy client into a happy client. It always helped to remember that clients are often reacting to feelings of fear or insecurity, and their momentary anger and upset should be met with compassion.

JILL R. FOREMAN, MBA, CVPM
Danville, Pennsylvania

Our clients are simply pet owners who are experiencing something troublesome in their relationships with their pets—whether it is a sudden injury, a chronic illness, or even trying to snag their unwilling pets from under the bed and into a carrier to come in for routine vaccinations. They often must subject their pets to pokes and prods, injections and invasions, all in an effort to keep or make them healthy. Unlike two-legged children, pets never can understand why their pet parents are putting them in this situation. We ask our clients to leave their beloved pets in our capable and caring hands, but it is still scary for them. If we can always approach our clients with understanding and compassion, we will help the entire family through whatever struggle they're facing.

Veterinary medicine is wonderful when you see a favorite patient get better and go home. We had a yellow lab as a patient that was a rock eater. He came in for his second surgery to remove rocks, and you could hear the rocks clinking together in his stomach as he walked down the hall. It was morbidly funny. He had over a dozen in there, but he recovered just fine from surgery.

Elise M. Atkinson, BA, CVT
Lakewood, Colorado

We sometimes see, and hear, the most amazing things in veterinary medicine! Another case involved a dog that ate a whole box of carpenter staples and then had to endure more than two hours of endoscopy as they were extracted. Just knowing we can help animals who eat foreign bodies is a wonderful feeling. Without us, they wouldn't stand a chance with their crazy appetites!

There is only one way to enhance communication between the doctors and staff, and that is to talk to the veterinarian yourself. Don't tell someone in hopes that he or she will tell the vet. You need to take that responsibility upon yourself, and don't tell just one vet . . . if there is more than one, tell all of them.

BESSIE JANE DEVOLL, RVT
Zanesville, Ohio

It is easy to hide behind someone else when a difficult conversation has to happen, particularly when a veterinarian or practice owner needs to be involved. The easiest route may seem to be to talk to a supervisor or manager, hoping that the conversation will happen without you and things will change for the better. Yet this is not always the best way. If you participate in that conversation directly, you can be sure the message is accurate and the delivery is appropriate, and your owner or doctor may gain respect for you even if he or she doesn't agree with what you're saying. At the very least, make sure that the "little things" are communicated by you directly. If you feel a topic is too heavy or volatile, it may be appropriate to ask your supervisor or manager to facilitate a meeting between you and the veterinarian. This way the words are coming from you, but the mediator can make sure that the message is witnessed and may smooth over any potential rough spots. If the issue affects all the veterinarians on staff, the message must reach them all in one way or another, either directly from you or through a member of leadership. Silence only breeds difficulty and distress.

Our team loves our once-a-month "Eating Meetings," sponsored by vendors and suppliers. Each month a different team member gets to pick where we will order lunch. We have two special monthly awards that are passed on each month by the previous month's winner. One is the "Silver Poop Scoop" award. This is an actual silver cat poop scoop ceremoniously mounted on a wooden plaque. This is awarded to the team member who deals with the most poop, either literally or figuratively. It is proudly displayed for the entire month in the winner's work area. The "Whoopee" award is a whoopee cushion and a kazoo mounted in a box frame and is awarded to the team member who makes us laugh. Each winner is awarded $25 in bonus bucks and is recognized at every team meeting by the entire team with applause. Some of the speeches when these awards are passed on are hilarious!

Jennifer Johnson

This team has certainly developed some creative ways to encourage fun *and* recognition in their practice! They recognize that the daily grind can contain unpleasant aspects such as poop, but also that humor can help them all through the tough times. In your practice, create an award or come up with your own creative way of recognizing those team members who go above and beyond in helping either the patients or the team.

"

On hard days, such as when staff members would call off their shift at the last minute, I would remind myself of the rewarding moments. To that end, I kept thank-you cards near my desk so I could review the good things I had been able to accomplish during my tenure. By the same token, I always tried to improve the general atmosphere for employees. This is stressful work, and if I was able to make someone's day better or accommodate [his or her] special request, it was gratifying.

JILL R. FOREMAN, MBA, CVPM
Danville, Pennsylvania

When we contribute to a good day for a coworker, everyone in the practice wins through improved morale. Just as you enjoy looking back at the memorabilia of thanks from clients who thought you are special, it's just as important to make others feel special, too.

Try to keep things lighthearted. Our work
can cause a lot of anxiety, stress, and sorrow.
When not in the "high speed" mode, relax
and enjoy your patients and each other.

GERIANNE HOLZMAN, CVT, VTS (DENTISTRY)
Madison, Wisconsin

Each member of the team possesses powerful positive energy. Among your coworkers there is likely a friend or colleague who has experienced the same frustrations you face, so it's important to share your feelings and move past differences to support each other. There is also a wealth of positive energy from our nearest and dearest source, our patients. Snuggling with a cat or petting a dog can be the best prescription for a wearisome day or a moment filled with doubt.

I have seen many pets arrive in our clinic for euthanasia,
die in our care, or arrive deceased. I show empathy
for the pain and loss the family is experiencing. I also
find that making clay [imprints of pets'] paws for the
clients allows me to grieve for the family's loss, and I
feel better knowing I am creating a memory for them.

ANDREA TUCKER, CLIENT CARE PROFESSIONAL
Colorado Springs, Colorado

We often create memorial gifts for our client families to express how much we care and to recognize the period of grief that the family will endure. Yet as Andrea mentions, creating these gifts can also allow us to recognize and express our own grief at our patient's passing. Often we are not just losing the pet; we may also lose touch with that family, unless they have other pets. So it can be a difficult transition for the team, especially if they have maintained close contact with that family through an extended illness or injury. They become part of our extended family, and suddenly it seems as though they have moved halfway across the country, even if they're still just down the street. This is a transition that should also be addressed and discussed by the veterinary team.

As a new graduate, I was asked by a veterinarian during an interview what I thought the toughest thing about working in a veterinary practice would be. I said the fast pace, or trying to balance the typical day-to-day activities with the inevitable emergencies. The doctor then told me what he thought the hardest part was— euthanasia. That one simple statement had touched me more than I knew, and I went to work for this practice because they had so much compassion for the animals. After I became the manager of this practice, I asked that same question in each and every interview.

LAURIE MILLER, RVT, CVT, CVPM
Tolleson, Arizona

Often, because we have been involved in veterinary medicine for a while, we forget a time when euthanasia was not a part of our professional lives. Veterinary medicine is the only medical profession that provides humane euthanasia to end suffering, and we often suffer because of our responsibility in administering this final act of love. We need to remember when we welcome new members into the veterinary profession that they have not yet faced this awesome responsibility, and we should support them on their journey to acceptance of ending our patients' suffering.

"

To manage stress I first of all try not to let it consume
me totally. I try to put the "stressor" into perspective
and realize, if it is not all that important, then I should
deal with it to the best of my ability and then let it go.
In the big picture of things, how important is it really?
Although this sounds good, in reality, sometimes it
is hard to achieve. In which case I just try to handle
the stress as well as I can and then just let it go.

HELEN R. DeWITT, BA, AS, AAS, CVT

"

As Helen suggests, the best intentions are sometimes thwarted. We all try to put things in perspective, but sometimes it is difficult. Letting go can also be a challenge. The way you handle stress will depend on your personality. If you tend to dwell on the negative and find it difficult to move forward, then you will need to work harder at finding and maintaining balance. Sometimes even the "happy person" on the team is just hiding his or her true feelings, because it's easier than dealing with them. So you have to take some time to know yourself and find the best methods for you to cope.

"

Working in the veterinary field is the one job that I have had that leaves me feeling fulfilled and relaxed at the end of the day. I find that any lingering stresses are usually related more to staff issues, as opposed to my actual work. If I do have a particularly stressful day for any reason, I settle in on the sofa with a glass of wine and my fifteen-year-old cat!

DONNA E. BROUSSARD, SENIOR TECHNICIAN
Dallas, Texas

"

Our profession uses the term *burnout* quite a bit. Burnout is "the state of physical and emotional and mental exhaustion caused by the depletion of ability to cope with one's environment resulting from our responses to the ongoing demand characteristics (stress) of our daily lives" (Maslach, 1982). Another concept that is similar, but also different, is "compassion fatigue," exhaustion due to compassion stress, the demands of being empathetic and helpful to those who are suffering (Figley and Roop, 2006). It's easier to tell the difference if you think of it this way: burnout is caused by *where* you work, whereas compassion fatigue is caused by the work you *do*. Management, co-workers, workload, assigned tasks, and resources or lack thereof can certainly lead you to feel burned-out. Those issues have to be handled head-on, at work. Compassion fatigue, however, is more personal. The best way to protect yourself and recover from compassion fatigue is to give yourself the same good care that you give others, and sometimes that is difficult for people who are "helpers." We worry more about them than about ourselves. Although Donna may feel burned-out on occasion because of circumstances at work, she has found a way to unwind and find some "me time" at the end of a stressful day. Some of us will need the help of professionals to address and diminish our personal compassion fatigue. It is not selfish to ask for help; it may be the only way to stay strong so you can continue in your career.

I stay inspired by thinking about the "big picture" and by realizing that we are truly helping people through their pets. I also think it is important that as a team, we have parties, activities, etc., together. This helps us to become close, so when one team member is feeling downtrodden or uninspired, we are there to help reinspire [him or her]. I make sure to take my vacation time and to not sweat the little stuff. I also take as much continuing education as I can. This helps me to stay inspired, knowing that I am truly offering the highest level of care to our clients and their furry family members.

Christina Chatham

It is easy to get bogged down in the details of the day, the tasks that need to be done, the chores that have to be completed, and the general frustrations that are part of any job. Yet when you step back and look at the "big picture," do you see how the care you give your patients translates into helping people in their time of need? We may not be instruments of world peace, but we do work miracles to help families stay together longer. Sometimes it helps if your coworkers remind you of this mission; if you have grown close rather than just remained distracted employees working side by side, you can help each other overcome some of the challenges of staying in this profession long term. You also have to take care of yourself. Use the vacation time that you have earned and try to take time away from the stresses of daily life. Spend time with your own pets and family, so you can reconnect with how important they all are to your life. It will be easier to go back to work when vacation is over when you know that you are helping others keep that family connection with their pets.

My inspiration comes from strengthening the bond
between an owner and his or her pet. Whether
it be getting the pet through a rough time like a
surgery or helping it to live longer so the owner
and pet can spend more time together.

NANCY A. MILLER, RVT
Davenport, Iowa

The human-animal bond is a strong tie. Our responsibility is to improve the quality or the quantity of the time people have with their pets. Even when a terminal or life-threatening condition is diagnosed, it's important that the family make the best of the time they have left together. It often helps to explain that their pet members do not realize the end is near and to counsel them to focus on the happy memories they can still make together. This will allow the family to enjoy their last months, weeks, or days together.

Our mission statement is strategically placed in the center of our treatment room (it is easily read from across the room). This is a constant reminder to those working and entering the treatment room why we are here and what we are about. This is especially important when we have those hectic, busy days with no time for ourselves, or a day when we have to say goodbye to many of our special patients.

Diane W. Culver, LVT
Syracuse, New York

Do you know your practice's mission? Does your practice have a mission, or a vision, objective, or common goal that you all share? Is there a guiding light that keeps you all on the right path, toward compassionate patient care and excellent client service? How well do you remember this mission during the tough days, the long hours, or the sad times of loss? The guiding light should help steer you and your team toward a higher purpose and make your hours at work meaningful. If your practice is lacking this guidance, perhaps it's time to start the conversation in your own work group. What motto do the technicians want to live by? "Treat every pet as if it were your own," perhaps? Maybe the front office team would have something like "All communication moves through us with an importance and purpose?" It's possible for staff in each position to determine their own working motto to help steer the way through the foggy days and difficult hours of veterinary work.

To find your niche in a practice, you need to discover what you enjoy the most and where you are the biggest asset. That way, not only do you get to do what you enjoy the most, you are also contributing to the practice by offering your best side!

RACHEL S. KINKADE, CVT
Surprise, Arizona

Job fit involves more than just determining if the practice is the right place for you. It also involves finding the right position within the practice for your skills and interests. Depending on the size and type of practice, there could be team members who do a little bit of everything while others specialize in a particular skill or area of knowledge. Start by examining where your interests lie, and then start searching for the right job fit. If you want to perform a variety of tasks, a smaller general practice may be the best place for you. If you have developed a specialized area of interest, then you may be looking for a larger general practice, or perhaps an emergency or specialty practice. Once you are on board, make your interests known to members of management and find out what it will take to assume the role you want most. Be sure to let them know that you will be a greater asset to the practice if you're able to use your interests and talents. Rebecca Rose, CVT, and Carin Smith, DVM, published a great book for technicians about exploring their job options, *Career Choices for Veterinary Technicians* (AAHA Press, 2009).

Realize that each employee is an individual who adds value to the whole team. Treat each according to his or her own unique personalities, communication styles, and issues. Hopefully this sends a message that you recognize and respect them all.

ALLI SERGENT, LVT
Las Vegas, Nevada

A team's members bring their own special styles and contributions to the practice. They should be recognized as individuals, who respond to different types of communication and incentives. Does one person appreciate a direct style of communication, whereas another needs more gentle coaxing? Is one person motivated by "things" such as rewards of gifts and gift cards, but another would most appreciate an extra afternoon off? It's important for the leaders, and indeed everyone at the practice, to recognize and respect the individual units that make up the team. The team can be successful, but each person must be challenged and motivated to be a success as well.

Some days are so difficult. I remember one day when I had to deal with five patient deaths—we had to perform three euthanasias plus we lost two patients. To get through the day, I just concentrated on working on the patients and attending to the clients. But sometimes I still wish I could wipe that day from my memory.

Mary Brussell
Lakewood, Colorado

Although it is very difficult when we lose patients, whether to natural death or euthanasia, it's okay and important for you to grieve for the pets who die in your care. This should be an intentional, deliberate process, not a feeling you try to avoid or deny. As you move forward past the loss, it helps to simply focus on the patients that are still with us and need our help and undivided attention. The patients themselves can become a great source of strength as we work tirelessly to help them. Clients often appreciate our dedication and assistance, even though they may have no idea what we have witnessed that day before their appointment.

Veterinary technology is a great profession. I am allowed to do so much as a CVT. The staff sees all of the technician's responsibilities and is grateful for everything that we do. It's great having been in the field for ten years and having new veterinary graduates come and ask for my opinion on certain cases. It's a very rewarding career, with so many advancement opportunities.

Amanda Henry, CVT
Janesville, Wisconsin

In most states it takes a lot of hard work to become a credentialed veterinary technician. After all that effort, it is rewarding to be recognized and respected for what you can contribute to the care of patients and clients. It is particularly pleasant when those who are new to the practice of veterinary medicine recognize that your experience and expertise can also help them do their best. Whether you are a new veterinary school graduate or a new veterinary technician, there is a time to put aside individual pride and realize that others can help you learn to be the best you can be. There will also be a time when it's your turn to shine! Then it will be imperative for you to teach others what you know, so everyone can do their best for your patients and clients.

Fortunately, I work in a very progressive practice
and all the veterinarians are already on board
with full utilization of veterinary technicians.
However, at any seminars or meetings I attend, I
use that opportunity to network with veterinarians
about how great it is for both the technicians and
veterinarians when we get to utilize all of our skills.

LINDA HENNESSY, RVT
Pleasant Hill, California

This is a wonderful way of promoting the veterinary technology profession to those whose opinion matters most, the veterinarians. Take the opportunity to give veterinarians feedback about how useful technicians can be in their practice, with real-life examples from your own practice if possible. If you're in a position to brag to others, then by all means do it. If you need your practice to utilize you more, hopefully one of your veterinarians will come across Linda at a seminar! You can certainly advocate for yourself at your own practice in the meantime.

Veterinary technicians must bond together and get
the word out about our profession. Most people
don't even know our profession exists. We should be
proud of the work we do and promote it whenever
the chance arises. We should talk to other technicians
and assistants whenever we are together, bounce ideas
off each other, and use others' ideas when possible.

VICKI JONES, RVT
Emporia, Kansas

The veterinary technology profession is only as strong as the bonds among veterinary technicians. We must understand that educating the public is an important step toward a better future for our profession. The more people know the type of care their pets can receive from a qualified technician, the more they will insist on this type of care. It is also vital to realize that other technicians have wonderful ideas to share to enhance our profession. Take opportunities to meet and discuss ideas and protocols. At a conference or seminar, you can learn just as much from the technician sitting next to you as you can from the person at the podium. Use these networking opportunities to share your thoughts and enhance our profession.

"

Sometimes when speaking to clients I like to start out saying, "What I learned in school was . . ." or "I recently read an article or attended a seminar and learned . . ." I find that some people seem to look at you like you're just a random person off the streets who learned how to draw blood, but if you mention something about your school and continuing education, they realize that this is actually a profession and requires school and training.

Christine Schultz, CVT
Darien, Illinois

Educating the general public about the role of the veterinary technician in practice is every credentialed technician's duty, in both small and big ways. The small ways are the more personal—giving people you come across every day in practice a glimpse of the dedication and challenge involved in becoming a credentialed technician. You can purchase a personalized name tag with your name, credentials, or position title to wear outside work, when you want to strike up a conversation about what you do for a living. Companies that sell scrubs often have these types of badges, or you can visit the Magic Zoo online (www.themagiczoo.com) for custom badges and jewelry. Perhaps your practice is involved in community outreach with other animal lovers or advocates; this is a great opportunity to educate others by wearing a name tag with your name and credentials, or perhaps a button or pin that signifies veterinary technicians, such as the veterinary technology "VT" caduceus. Get out into the community and teach others about the veterinary technology career. Schools are often looking for people to participate in career days and job fairs, or you can speak to groups such as scouts and clubs.

For my job at the front desk, I would recommend
a stomach of steel and a strong psyche. I see a lot
working the front desk of an emergency practice, and
it is very mentally taxing. There are days when I just
want to get up and walk out and never look back. As
a receptionist you take heat from clients, doctors, and
technicians, so the ability to let things roll off your
shoulders is a must; never take anything personally. It
is a tough job but the ability to be there for a family
in their moment of crisis is infinitely rewarding.

KATHERINE E. SMELTZER, CLIENT SERVICE REPRESENTATIVE
Leesburg, Virginia

The front office team faces a variety of challenges every day. Anyone coming through the door could turn out to be a grateful pet parent or a stressed-out person on the edge of mental breakdown, and the front office staff must be the first to step up and help. As if that weren't difficult enough, there are times when the other members of the team are also stressed to the point of treating the front office members harshly. Although this seems to come with the territory, it is amazing when the person sitting at that front desk can handle all of this and more. It takes a measure of stamina and positive attitude to handle whatever comes up.

The best way a person can be a valuable employee
is to truly enjoy the work you are doing. This will
show in the quality of your work and keep you
interested in learning new ways of doing your job.
If you are happy you will want to keep up with
the latest information and never stop learning.

KATHY SIMPSON, BSBA, RVT

Learning and job satisfaction form a cycle: when you continue to learn, you continue to be satisfied and are motivated to do a better job. The knowledge that you obtain from learning helps you to do a better job, and this leads back to satisfaction. This is one reason that continuing education is so important in keeping our profession and our professionals motivated on the job.

To be well prepared and reduce stress, look at the schedule for the day. If it looks busy, chances are it probably will be—plan for a few things, but don't plan a whole hospital cleanup; that's too much. And sometimes, especially in Minnesota, you have wonderful snow days when everyone calls off their appointments and you can do amazing things—but don't scare yourself with the amount of stuff to do.

Brenna Johnson, CVT
Phoenix, Arizona

I t's difficult to know how a day will turn out. Sometimes days with lots of appointments scheduled turn out to be slow after all, for example when it snows, whereas at other times an empty day on the schedule turns out crazy, with four emergency cases! The best idea is to have a list of projects that is always accessible to the staff so they can choose something to do when things are slow. Create an ongoing project list that contains both revolving tasks to be completed on a regular basis, such as weekly, monthly, or quarterly, and a list of one-time projects. Keep this list in a central location for the entire team to consult when it's slow. Of course, during a string of busy days don't expect that the team will be able to accomplish a lot of extra projects. Have a contingency plan in place; if the kennel has to be sterilized no matter what, don't hope for a slow period but instead schedule someone to have the time necessary to accomplish that project.

When faced with a difficult situation, breathe! Then take action to address it. Then meet with a confidant to vent. Then exercise . . . not necessarily in that order.

JULIET STERNBERG, LMSW
Brooklyn, New York

We will all face difficult situations during the course of our careeers, but how we handle the pressure will either set us apart or cause us to collapse. "Breathe" may sound simple enough, yet it's been proven that when faced with a stressful situation, we tend to hold our breath, which causes us to be less mentally prepared to take action. So take a couple of slow, deep breaths before responding. Find a private space (e.g., the bathroom), close your eyes, and breathe. Count to five as you slowly inhale, then count to five as you slowly exhale. Do this for eight cycles, and you'll be amazed at how this simple exercise can calm down your body and mind. If you're facing an unfamiliar situation, do your best or seek assistance. If you've been down this road before, remember your past successes and move forward with confidence. Afterward, it may be necessary to share the incident with others to let go of the tension. Just remember not to dump your stress on them so that it becomes their burden to bear. Better yet, let physical exertion work the stress out of your muscles. Perhaps a few laps around the parking lot are in order!

The most special thing about my job is comforting and relating with the clients. Perhaps it seems a little strange, but the difficult clients are my favorites. For me, these clients that are scared or angry to the extreme make my day, not because they are angry or obnoxious, but because to take someone from that extreme of an emotion and be able to put a smile on his or her face, to help him or her understand and cope with whatever trauma, big or small, is amazing. When you can do that, you have changed the way another person looks at not only you, but the entire veterinary field. You have impacted . . . [lives], so even if you do not remember them, they will always remember you.

KATHERINE E. SMELTZER, CLIENT SERVICE REPRESENTATIVE
Leesburg, Virginia

E very person on the veterinary team represents the profession at large. Although we may see a string of clients in and out, day after day, we have to appreciate every pet owner as an individual and every situation as unique and deserving of our personal concern. So we must work to make it as pleasant as possible, regardless of the circumstances, by providing whatever support is necessary. Each person on the team can improve his or her communication skills by attending seminars and training sessions that offer education in communication.

Respect is earned. If you do not respect the hospital
and doctors, you are in the wrong hospital.

VIRGINIA JONES
Monroe, Washington

Respect is imperative, and it must go both ways. It seems we spend so much time making sure we are respected, we forget that we must also respect our employer, or we won't be a good fit long term. There are many reasons why respect may be difficult or impossible to develop. If the practice's morals and ethics don't agree with our own beliefs, it will never be a good fit. It is difficult to put aside how we feel pets and clients should be treated when faced with a practice that may not share our views. If your employer has not earned your respect, you should consider whether this is the right place for you.

I think that, as a technician, if you act in a professional manner and always strive to do your best work, then you will begin to earn the respect of your doctors. You need to walk a fine line between advocating for your patients and making the doctors feel like you are questioning their decisions. I try to always put things in the form of a question. For example, "Would you like me to give Fluffy a dose of buprenorphine?" vs. "I think we should give Fluffy some buprenorphine." Doctors are usually very busy and have a lot on their minds. A good vet will rely on technicians to anticipate what they need and catch what they have missed. I think you also earn respect from veterinarians when you show that you want to learn more and challenge yourself.

LYNN M. PRESNELL, RVT
Baltimore, Maryland

As Lynn's example demonstrates, sometimes it's more important *how* you say something when you are advocating for your patient. You do not want the veterinarian to feel you are questioning his or her medical authority, yet you want to let him or her know that you have concerns on behalf of the patient. In the end, the most important thing is that the patient receives the necessary care, and positive communication skills will help make this a reality without straining the professionals' relationships within the team.

Don't be afraid to talk. Whenever my doctor starts shutting off the communication line, I call him out on it. I ask him what he needs, what room he is in, and then I crack a joke. It gets him out of his foul mood and reminds him that I am here to help, not hinder.

KAREN LYNN MOES, VETERINARY ASSISTANT,
CLIENT SERVICE TECHNICIAN
Holland, Michigan

This is a good example of how we use humor to get past rough spots or speed bumps in our daily routine. Often a veterinarian can be blindsided by a troublesome patient, client, or event. If you can be a grounding force, a lightning rod in a manner of speaking, you can divert that negative energy and prevent it from ruining the rest of everyone's day. Often a team will develop silent signals or inside jokes that help rouse someone from a bad mood or moment. This demonstrates the strength of strong partnerships and team relationships.

We hula hoop at lunchtime. It's a great stress reliever and fun exercise. We leave silly notes for each other and work great as a team, helping each other without asking. Also "switching up the schedules," changing from daylight to afternoon shift, gives everyone a chance to see things through somebody else's eyes.

Stacey Oden, CVT
Wexford, Pennsylvania

A team that laughs together, stays together. Stress is a reality of our jobs, and looking for ways to relieve stress on the job can be very helpful to team members. We also must try not to expend every ounce of energy at work, so that we have something for ourselves, our friends, and our families when the shift is over. The ability to recharge at work with something as simple as a hula hoop can help improve the energy level and the outlook of our team members.

We find creative ways to stay motivated. For instance, we set weekly goals and when they are reached, everyone gets to pick from a grab bag. The items usually cost $1 to $2. Staff can also give complimentary examinations on business cards printed with their names to members of the general public. Once a month we do a drawing of the cards turned in for a Starbucks or Dairy Queen gift card. On the back of my office door is a shoe pocket for each staff member. It's fun to slip a quick note of encouragement or a piece of candy, etc., in the pockets for staff to find. And CE credits earned from online courses can be turned in for credit on their account in the form of Animal Medical Bucks. The credit can be used for products and services for their own pets, and they get an education at the same time.

LAUREN MATTACCHIONE, OFFICE MANAGER
Chesapeake, Virginia

Lauren has given us some good ideas about how to weave fun and recognition into the culture of a practice, along with a marketing tip or two! Our leadership can often find creative ways to enhance that all-important team buy-in for new initiatives or continuous team rewards. It doesn't take much to make someone's day; a thoughtful trinket is often worth more than a poorly delivered compliment. Borrow one of Lauren's ideas, or come up with your own, to encourage team recognition and reward in your practice.

At my practice, a hug really does do the job for
clients who are grieving the loss of their pet or
the unexpected news that their pet is ill. We
pride ourselves on our "high-touch" practice, and
that does not limit us to just our patients.

JOANNE LIGHT, LVT
Las Vegas, Nevada

When you've spent time with a family, watching their beloved pet grow from a frisky pup or playful kitten into an older, more gentle animal, it can be very difficult to watch the pet succumb to illness or injury. By this time, you are often part of this pet's extended family. Although some families may not be the "hugging type," many clients will appreciate this expression of affection and understanding. If you're the hugging type too, give it a try.

Compassion fatigue is a concern, but I know in my heart that we are helping those we can, and providing comfort for those we can't, by performing humane euthanasia. For me, there have been many tears and lots of frustration, but it helps to know I am making a difference in people's lives during their time of need.

TANIA HMUROVICH, CVA

Tania's comments illustrate an important point: that we are more able to cope with the euthanasia we provide if we feel it is the right thing to do for our patients and we are making a positive difference in our clients' lives. A survey of compassion fatigue in the animal care community showed that one of the main reasons we are satisfied with our careers is the animals we help and the clients who are thankful. These survey results and more can be found in *Compassion Fatigue in the Animal-Care Community* by Charles R. Figley, PhD, and Robert G. Roop, PhD (The Humane Society of the United States, 2006). Sometimes we don't even know we have helped a family until long after the fact, when we get a thank-you card expressing how important it was that we helped them through their pet's euthanasia. These moments of appreciation are special and can help us cope with the compassion fatigue that is a natural by-product of the work we do.

When I need to, I go to my happy place, momentarily
forgetting about everything surrounding me. I take
slow, deep breaths, and concentrate on the reason
I am here and not on what else is going on.

CASEY L. PALMER, CVT

Everyone should have a "happy place" where he or she can seek solace when there is craziness all around. Even just a few moments with your eyes closed, either visualizing a scenic escape or picturing the stress flowing out of your body, can help ground you. We always know the reason we are "here," in the profession, yet sometimes that reason gets buried in the chaos of the moment. We must find ways to release the stress if we are to remain resilient in this career.

Education is truly the key to staying inspired. As we keep ourselves abreast of "what's new" and network with our colleagues—essentially, elicit change—we progress and see improvement in patient care. And patient care and animal welfare are what it's all about.

Michelle M. Earltinez, CVT
Cocoa, Florida

We do create change every time we take a new concept or new application of a standard concept and use it to enrich the lives of our patients and their families. We are each the future of veterinary medicine, and we must do our part to stay educated and informed. All the studies, discoveries, and scientific breakthroughs are nothing without those of us who apply this new knowledge every day with the patients in our care. Take time to marvel at how far we've come in our efforts to help pets, and never take for granted the important part you play in the profession.

To counteract stress, go out for lunch; listen to music; count to ten; soak in a hot tub at the end of the day.

CINDY GOLDSTEIN, LVT
Lynbrook, New York

B esides being able to step away during the workday for some rest and relaxation, Cindy has learned how important it is for us to develop a "transition routine" at the end of the day. This may be playing music on the drive home, stopping for a walk along a trail, or sitting in your backyard for a few minutes before going in—whatever it takes for you to be able to put aside your day and then focus on others who need you, including yourself. Take some time to think of a transition routine for yourself. What can you do at the end of your work shift to smooth the transition from your workday to the rest of your day, when you will enjoy time with your family, friends, children, and pets? Then stick to the routine and see if it makes a difference in your move from work to home life.

Remember it is not about you, it is about your patients.
Your patient does not care what kind of day you are
having, and you should never expect him or her to.

KIMBERLY SCHMIDT, CVT
Fort Collins, Colorado

When you are involved in a helping profession, you have to give of yourself even when you're not in the mood. You must be entirely present each day you're on the floor, because your patients aren't going to be less sick or needy just because you're having a rough day. There will be time to focus on your needs when your patients and clients are either discharged or handed over to other capable hands. Remember, no matter how tough a day is, at some point it will end . . . and then when you clock out, it's time to switch gears and think about yourself.

I handle the long hours at the veterinary hospital calmly, with plenty of sleep, vitamins, eating right, and a good attitude. This is not an eight-to-five field, and we are here for the clients and patients. Even the smallest ailments are an emergency to a client when it involves their pet. So some days it may be slow, but when it rains, it can pour. Smile!

LYNDI M. WATSON, LVT
Tampa, Florida

One of the challenges of this career is that the days, or nights if you're on the overnight shift, can be extremely long. You're often fortunate if you're scheduled for only eight hours, and even as the end of the shift nears, you wonder if you'll actually get to leave on time. Lyndi has the right idea: take care of yourself so that your body (and soul) can withstand the pressure of this profession. Tell yourself that your patients and clients need you to be your best, so trick yourself into doing it for them. A healthy body leads to a healthy attitude, and our patients and clients really will enjoy the benefits. Most important, you and your family and friends will appreciate the outcome!

I always tell new technicians that "the day that euthanasia doesn't make you at least a little emotional, that's the day you should look for another job." There will always be clients and patients that we really come to love. For me, it's that emotional connection with patients that drives me to help make their lives better, even if that means providing them some final relief. Even clients I have never met before who struggle with euthanasia evoke a certain level of sympathy, simply because I am human and a pet owner. Putting myself in their shoes helps me understand how difficult a decision it was for them. Having the strength and courage to invest emotionally in clients and patients just a little bit is what makes a great technician, but finding a balance is the hard part.

CHANTELLE TEBALDI, CVT
Boston, Massachusetts

Technicians are bound by the Veterinary Technician Oath to alleviate animal suffering: "I solemnly dedicate myself to aiding animals and . . . alleviating animal suffering." Yet we must remain aware of our own suffering as we provide care. By connecting with our feelings and expressing them in positive ways, we can remain in this profession to continue our caring. Create a memory book to hold photos of patients you tended to and cards you received from appreciative clients. This will help you stay tuned in to the important work you do for pets and their families.

Morale is kept up through remembering manners:
please, thank you, etc., and offering compliments
and bonuses. Chocolate usually works wonders.

CAROLYN SMITH, VETERINARY ASSISTANT
AND VETERINARY TECHNOLOGY STUDENT
Winchester, Virginia

Ah, chocolate can work wonders, and there are few veterinary practices where food does not work well to calm even the toughest beasts and roughest days. It seems to be an inside joke in our profession that the way to our team's hearts is definitely through their stomachs. Vendors have learned that if they buy the practice lunch, they can gain access to the team, and we can certainly use this method ourselves. And yes, common (or these days, not so common) courtesies such as please and thank you are still welcome and sorely needed.

I do my duties during euthanasia with as gentle, quiet, and comforting a touch or motion as possible. Generally, I do not say much to the people involved, but simply appear that I understand their situation (because I do). I ask them if they want Kleenex, water, time to just be with the animal. Most of all I treat their animal with the same respect that I have for my own animals—with dignity, comfort, and love. However, I most often have tears in my eyes and can't speak much anyway.

DAWN MARIE PERAULT, BS, CVT
Maplewood, Minnesota

It is a special act to be there for someone at such a time of need. Sometimes it is difficult to know just what to do or what to say, but we can let our hearts guide us to do the most appropriate thing. Some families appreciate a hug, others just the quiet comfort of having you stand by to listen to their stories. Even once the pet has passed from this world, we treat it as fragile and precious, and demonstrate our respect for the patient and family. Is it okay to shed a tear or two yourself? Absolutely, because you do care about this family, and it's okay to care. You're also demonstrating that you understand their situation and how difficult it is to make these decisions on behalf of our pets. There are many factors involved in difficult decisions such as euthanasia and exposing pets to diagnostics or invasive therapies. *Kindred Spirit, Kindred Care*, by Shannon Fujimoto Nakaya, DVM (New World Library, 2005), is a wonderful resource. It is written for pet owners, so it is also for all of us who have pets of our own or are trying to understand how to interact with pet families.

We are "family." As a family-type unit, we are
very close; therefore we are able to laugh at each
other, with each other, and of course cry with one
another. We always try to make time to laugh, even
if to an outsider it would be a "stupid" joke.

REBECCA PLUMB, LVT, VTS (ECC)
Commerce, Michigan

Inside jokes often become ingrained in the culture of a veterinary practice. They are a result of shared experience and tend to grow richer over the years. These jokes naturally come up during the daily routine. Humor is used to smooth over some of the difficult events and grueling days experienced at the veterinary practice, letting the team pause and remember the lighter times in life.

Attitude, courtesy, and respect are the best ways to enhance communication between the "front and back" of the veterinary practice. A positive attitude is essential. Both groups are professionals and should be treated as such. Be sure to thank and express appreciation for all positive contributions. Finally, all need to be treated with respect as both groups are vital for a successful and thriving practice.

MARK HORTON, BS, CVT
Englewood, Colorado

Too often we hear about the "front versus back" issue in veterinary medicine. Unfortunately, it is true that in many practices these very different positions are not mutually respected by all members of the team. It's important to encourage a culture that reflects that we are all in this together. No one position is more important, or more difficult, or more special; it takes a team to make the veterinary practice work. Management or leaders of the team should seek input and opinions from every member of the team, regardless of the topic. Technicians may be affected when decisions are made in the front office about paper flow or client traffic, and the front office team has a stake in decisions that affect patients and result in additional explanation or invoicing up front. If everyone plays a part, there will be more fusion of the team.

Respect for the technician must be earned! This
means anticipating the needs of the doctors, going
the extra mile, setting up for procedures before they
ask, and following their directions without grumbling
or complaining. Also remember that each doctor
is unique and has his or her way of doing things.
Don't suggest the doctor do things a certain way
until he or she has confidence in your ability.

DIANE W. CULVER, LVT
Syracuse, New York

J ust as a manager must earn respect from the team, the veterinary technician must earn respect from the veterinarians. Diane points out that this can be done by being the best technician possible. We must also tread lightly at times, or at least avoid stepping on toes, while the doctor's trust in us is building.

The bond that I create with our clients is what means the most to me. There is nothing better than to have a client call back into the clinic after leaving or writing a note to thank our team for the service we provided. It means a lot to me to know that I was there helping someone during a time of great need for them.

ANDREA TUCKER, CLIENT CARE PROFESSIONAL
Colorado Springs, Colorado

Sometimes we have become so close to a family that they remember us, and we remember them, long after the pet that brought us together is gone from this world. That is certainly a treasure. You have made a lasting impact on that family with your care and concern, and they are now a part of your life and will always have a special place in your heart and memory.

With two children (three including my husband)
and a full-time job, it is difficult to paint my nails,
let alone read my *Vet Tech* or *Firstline* magazine! I set
aside my educational magazines, and when I have a
free minute, I pull them out. I really enjoy reading
them, so it's like "me time," which we all need.

JENNIFER HENZE, LVT
Gloversville, New York

Jennifer has the right attitude, even if her nails do go unpainted at times! Keep journals with you and take advantage of those moments that you can fill by expanding a few brain cells. You probably didn't choose this career as much as it chose you, or you experienced a calling of sorts. That is why allowing yourself the opportunity to bask in new knowledge can feel like "me time." Treat yourself to that "me time" away from the hustle and bustle of the practice, to enhance your knowledge and stay motivated in the profession.

Difficult clients are just people going through a trauma, and some people don't deal well with these situations. We become the target at the front desk because we're "available," but I turn the situation around and let the clients vent, cry, and speak their mind and I just listen. I offer empathy, a cup of coffee (decaf!), and tissues. Usually they calm down if you retain a calm demeanor yourself, and use kind but firm words to show them you really care. Many clients have apologized for being rude and thanked me after it's all over for taking care of them.

Tania Hmurovich, CVA

M ost difficult interactions are with clients enduring a stressful time, even if the source of that stress isn't evident to us. Often it directly involves their pets and the reason they are visiting us. At other times it's some unknown event or factor in their lives that we cannot identify and have no need to know. What we *do* need to know is how not to take their difficult behavior personally; it's not about us, it's about them, and our job is to make their experience in our practice the best possible. As Tania has experienced, often when the tense moment passes, these clients are the most thankful for us just being there for them during that difficult time.

As a member of the front office team, I can change people's day and the outlook they have for their loved one, no matter the circumstance, with the choice of words used when they walk through the door. I might not be able to diagnose, treat, or even [help them financially], but with my knowledge and experience I can present every option I know and help them feel less lost and alone. With this, I am able to feel accomplishment and self-worth in my career. I am proud of what I do. I know in my heart just how important I am to the flow of this hospital and other receptionists are to any clinic in the world. We are the first and last impression made on these clients; we are there as a shoulder to cry on, their advocate for the doctor, and the calming voice on the phone to help direct them.

KATHERINE E. SMELTZER, CLIENT SERVICE REPRESENTATIVE
Leesburg, Virginia

Even when we don't have the answer, or the answer the family wants to hear most, we can help them feel less alone in their time of need. We can display empathy in our actions and words, with open body language, comforting eye contact, and appropriate tone of voice. We know not to judge the family's decisions during a difficult time, realizing how difficult it would be for us as pet owners and that we simply cannot relate to their particular reality. Our choice of words should demonstrate our sympathy and understanding. Providing this necessary emotional support and comfort is a rewarding part of being on the front lines of the veterinary practice.

The best part of working in the veterinary profession is the ability to help educate the clients and to see a visible difference in the lives of the animals and their families. I'll always remember when I performed CPR on a DOA and it worked! The dog stayed in ICU for a few days and then was able to walk out on its own and live a long life.

RACHEL SCHULTZ, CVT, MM, CVPM
Elbridge, New York

The impact we have on our patients, as we work to save and extend lives on a daily basis, is sometimes astonishing. This family was able to make many more special memories with their beloved pet because Rachel and her practice were there to provide medical care. Sometimes you hope desperately that you can bring an injured or ill pet back to its family, and it's wonderful when hope combines with talent and caring to produce a miracle.

We can promote the profession of veterinary
technology by having technicians who truly love
their job, as I do, spread the word. To let people
know how needed we are, for the sake of the pets.

TINA MICROUTSICOS, BS, CVT
Princeton, New Jersey

The promotion of the profession must come from within, and each of us has a voice to contribute to the conversation. This voice can be raised at many events in the community. Offer to set up a booth about veterinary care at a community or county fair. Events such as dog and cat shows can also display information about our profession. The pets need each and every one of us, so we must let their "parents" know that we are here to help pets live longer and healthier lives!

Strive to be all that you can be every day! The more professionally you behave and appear, and the attitude you bring to your job every day, will influence everyone around you! You must know that you are a professional who has taken the challenge of higher learning to make a difference to the animals and the owners who love them. Remember what makes us the amazing support staff that we are along with the special skills we have acquired; we make a difference! Be proud of how far we have come in this profession. In a perfect environment, the doctors you work with will treat you as a professional and set the example for your practice.

Teresa A. Marcolini, CVT

The perfect practice will include veterinarians who understand that technicians are skilled professionals, and they will establish a tone of mutual respect. If the veterinarians in your practice are still working to understand the importance of technicians, don't let that stop you from being a good role model to the rest of the technicians and the entire team. Creating a respectful environment has to start somewhere, and it doesn't always have to be at the top! As Teresa says, behave and appear as a professional, and you will be more respected as a professional. This includes not just how you look and act "on the clock," but also how you represent your practice and your profession to the outside veterinary world and the general public. When you attend continuing education seminars or conferences, represent your employer and your profession well. When you are asked by a member of the general public where you work or what you do, speak with pride about your practice and your profession. Together we do make a difference, and even separately we can make a difference in our own little corner of the world.

When the veterinarians are able to focus only on those tasks they can do (diagnose, prescribe, perform surgery), the number of cases that we can handle increases, and therefore our revenue increases. My value is also determined by the level of trust placed in me by other people. The more the veterinarians trust me, the more they will delegate to me. The more clients trust me, the more likely that they will feel comfortable leaving their pet with me. It's also critically important that the entire veterinary healthcare team has good working relationships with one another. A poorly functioning team, made inefficient and ineffective by lack of leadership, communication issues, training inconsistencies, etc., can have a huge negative impact on a practice, so I also increase my personal value when I focus less on myself and more on the team.

Elizabeth Warren, RVT
Austin, Texas

The concept of using technicians to maximize veterinarian productivity is important and can lead to maximizing the potential profitability of a practice. When searching for ways to convince veterinarians to use their technicians' skills and knowledge, this is an important part of that conversation. Clients' trust should not be underestimated, either. Gaining their trust is an important first step in obtaining access to those pets that we can help. Finally, Elizabeth has expressed how focusing on the team effort makes a difference in the lives of people and pets.

"

Everyone from the kennel, from the assistants to the
receptionists to the technicians to the veterinarians,
is responsible for keeping that practice running.
It takes a team to keep animals healthy.

DONNA J. ROY, RVT
Torrance, California

We often talk about a medical hierarchy in the veterinary practice, starting at the top with the DVM. There is a specific person in charge when it comes to making medical decisions and giving medical opinions. Yet when it comes to the team that delivers care, everyone is important. There is a symbiotic relationship in which each person helps others reach their potential.

If team members don't believe in our
philosophy, they don't end up staying.

MONIQUE PIERPONT, RVT AND TEAM LEADER
Jupiter, Florida

When enough members of the team live and demonstrate the mission, it is difficult for those who don't believe in the mission to stay on the team. A process of self-selection takes place, as those who don't fit in are weeded out or quit because the job fit isn't right. That's not to say that their skills were insufficient or their knowledge incomplete; perhaps the culture was not right for them. Job fit is important, and it's often difficult to determine with a new hire until some time has passed. The team should be able to see if the new person fits into the culture, and the new person should be able to determine if the job is a good fit for him or her and make the right decision for everyone's benefit.

A good clinic focuses on the client/pet relationship and how it relates to that hospital. Focusing on only receiving and making money instead of providing amazing and personal service does not make a hospital great. The people who work there and the loyal clientele make for a wonderful clinic.

BRENNA JOHNSON, CVT
Phoenix, Arizona

Although veterinary medicine is certainly a business and must be profitable to remain open, it's important to know the values of the practice owners and the culture they have created. Fortunately, providing amazing client service most often results in a profitable business. It's imperative that the end goal be taking care of clients and patients, not just the balance in the bank.

I usually tell others that we are only as strong as our weakest member. To give our patients the best care possible we need to function well together as a team.

JENNIFER YORAWAY, CVT
Eden Prairie, Minnesota

Regardless of position title, everyone plays an important role on the veterinary healthcare team. Teamwork is more than just a group of individuals working toward the same goal; it is the synergy that creates something more than the sum of the individuals involved. Just as a chain is only as strong as its weakest link, so a team is only as strong as its weakest member. This is why it's important that everyone work together to create the strongest team. When your input is requested during training or evaluation of one of your teammates, it's important to be honest and factual. Everyone has a role in helping create and maintain the strongest team, and everyone's opinion matters to the leaders of the practice.

The owners of my patients didn't care if I had a hard or
bad day; I still needed to be there for their loved ones.
That's what I would want if the roles were reversed.

ELISE M. ATKINSON, BA, CVT
Lakewood, Colorado

It is often difficult to move through our day from task to task, and sometimes from one emotion to another, as we help the many families we will see during a shift. This may be the tenth family we've helped today, but this may be their only visit to the veterinary practice for the entire year or perhaps six months. It is up to us to make it as good an experience as possible. We must walk fresh into that room, not carrying our load from hours of work, and make the visit memorable for each client.

More candidates can be attracted to veterinary technology by stressing it *is* medicine. There is a perception that you just make appointments and play with dogs. It should be stressed it's a technical medical field.

R. M. (ANN) GILLESPIE, MS, RVT
Fort Valley, Georgia

As we all know, the veterinary technician does much more than make appointments and play with dogs! Yet how often do you take advantage of opportunities to share this information with others? There may be creative ways to piggyback on human healthcare events to make the veterinary profession better known. Find out whether your community has any type of "health fair" or similar activity at which you can spotlight our profession. You may get quite a bit of notice if you're the one whose patients have fur! If more people realize how closely our profession follows human nursing, they might be interested in joining us in the cause of helping pets and their people.

Respect for all team members goes a long way toward
working successfully as a team. No one position
in the clinic is better than any other position.

CAROL F. NEWSOM, BS, RVT

Each person's contribution to the team is vital. Often a team member may not have a clear idea of what the other people on the team are contributing. Job swapping and cross-training have been presented as ways for team members to gain some valuable perspective, but on a more mundane level, it takes only a moment of observation and real empathy to create that window of perception.

Very few people come to our hospital for a happy reason, so, in context, most of the difficult client behavior we see is totally justified. In fact, I've seen many truly devastated people be more composed and gracious than one would think possible. It is very gratifying to be a part of a team that works so hard to make the worst moments in our clients' lives better, less terrifying, and easier to bear.

LAURA GOODMAN, CLIENT SERVICE REPRESENTATIVE
Leesburg, Virginia

If we put ourselves in their position, it's remarkable that clients can demonstrate composure during some of the tragic and sad events that bring them to our door. How often this occurs in your practice depends on what type of practice it is; for example, an emergency and critical care practice sees pet owners more often during the most horrific experiences. They are often terrified, and providing them with comfort has a huge impact on their lives and helps them endure the difficult event.

Managers should not seek out to be loved; instead, strive to be respected. Your job is not to be popular. Your job is to improve your company to the best of your ability, and your staff is a key component to your success or your failure. If employees and managers have the company's best interests in mind, they should be able to work together toward a common goal. Employees need to accept that the manager's role is to help each employee be the best he or she can be. Managers need to be sensitive to each employee's feelings, cognizant of each employee's strengths and weaknesses, consistent in treating all employees equally, and inspiring of a positive and excellent environment and work ethic. Be an example for them.

Angie Shirley
Valparaiso, Indiana

J ust as money can't buy you love, the position title of manager or credentials behind your name can't buy you respect—and respect is imperative if you are going to lead a team to success. Your team members may not all like you, but as long as they respect you they will work toward a common goal, with your leadership and support. As a manager, you must also be a role model. You must be the type of employee you would hire or promote!

Veterinary practice can be challenging, to say the least.
So far, the worst day in my veterinary career was a day
when we were short-staffed, I worked a double shift, and
I had to help euthanize thirteen animals (all due to health
issues). It took an extreme emotional toll on me, and
it was *very* difficult for me to be there for every client,
not to mention keep my sanity. In order to mentally
survive this day, I didn't let myself get wrapped up in
the situation at the time. But after I got home I took a
long bath and hugged my boxer for a long, long time.

RACHEL SCHULTZ, CVT, MM, CVPM
Elbridge, New York

We can all relate to Rachel's bad day in one way or another. Being short-staffed seems to be a constant in the veterinary practice, and when no one else is available to help, you find yourself giving even more of your time to the practice. It's never easy to say goodbye to a family's pet, and certainly a string of them in one day can be overwhelming. Sometimes it's easier to just put yourself on "auto pilot" and try to fly through the day until it ends. Then you can retire to a safe space where you can process your emotions. Our pets at home are a welcome retreat.

By looking for the best in everyone and keeping a smile on my face, the fun follows. Sometimes someone will bring in a treat, and we post comical articles and such in the break room.

MARY MUIR, LVT
Shoreline, Washington

When something makes us laugh, we get more mileage from it by being able to share the humor. It's good to have a place on the employee bulletin board where lighthearted, humorous items can be shared (all in good taste, of course!). Create a space for your team to post humorous cartoons, articles, or pictures. Mary makes a good point that your outlook is important: if you always look for the best in people, you will rarely be disappointed!

There are days I walk out of my work doors and feel like I just need to break down and cry. . . . I find what can help is going to the gym, grabbing coffee with a good friend who will just sit and listen, or even writing pages upon pages in a journal. I must say this is the most psychologically challenging job I have ever had, but the smiles of the clients and tail wags of the patients we are able to help make everything worthwhile . . . I would not trade my job for the world.

KATHERINE E. SMELTZER, CLIENT SERVICE REPRESENTATIVE
Leesburg, Virginia

One of Katherine's tools for working through the challenges of being a front office team member is writing in a journal. Julia Cameron, a renowned author on spiritual creativity, has a method of journaling called "Morning Pages." The instructions appear in her book *The Artist's Way* (Penguin Books, 2007). According to Julia, the writing of morning pages is a way to tap our inner creativity and realize where we are now in a spiritual sense. As Julia comments, "We may have moved through our lives unconsciously for a while, perhaps for a great while, and so we must find and take up a tool that tells us where we are and how we actually feel about that." The basic theory is simple: morning pages are three full-sized pages of longhand, stream-of-consciousness writing that locate us precisely in the here and now. They are written first thing in the morning upon waking and can serve as a form of meditation for many. They don't have to make sense at all; they are truly just your first thoughts of the day as they come pouring out. Journaling has proven helpful for many in releasing stress and recentering their lives.

I remain inspired to stay on in the field every time a
client thanks me for helping save his or her animal
friend or every time I go into a cage to do a treatment
and I hear the cat purring or the dog licks my hand.

David M. Lawrence, CVT

Inspiration can come from something we expect, such as an expression of gratitude or thank-you card, or from many other places, when we're not looking. Take time to look around you and focus on those appreciative clients you have had the pleasure to help. Stop and spend a moment with the grateful patients. They may not be able to verbalize their gratitude, but you can see in their eyes when they know that you care.

Avoiding burnout is a work in progress for me.
Home, family, our own pets, work, pet sitting,
meetings, client/patient home care . . . the list goes
on. Loving, caring, nurturing, by nature we take on
more than we should. Don't compartmentalize; they
all need to be seen as a whole, a delicate balance of
each. Reprioritize when necessary, placing yourself
somewhere in the middle, not first so you feel selfish,
but not last so there is nothing left of you to give.

LISA TUCKER, RVT
Cumming, Georgia

Balance, a concept that Lisa describes perfectly, is the key to maintaining our resiliency in this profession. If we're able to look beyond the moment, to the big picture, we will see things more clearly. If we're able to see ourselves as whole, rather than as unconnected pieces, we will be better able to hold ourselves together. You must love and care for yourself as you do your patients, because they depend on you . . . and *you* depend on you!

Some days I handle it better than other days. On my good days, I try to keep a sense of humor about everything. If things are really intense, then I try to take a break. I walk away and try to work on something else, or just take a patient outside for a walk. That way it is good for both patient and caretaker.

RENE SCALF, CVT, VTS (ECC, SAIM)
Fort Collins, Colorado

A great way to reconnect with the reason we're here, and to give yourself a break, is to do as Rene recommends and take a patient for a walk, or stop to give a cage-bound patient a few moments of your time. It is good for both of you! Humor is prevalent in our profession, and that must be because it helps us all deal with the reality of the work we do. If we can keep each other laughing, even between the hard moments, we will rejuvenate our spirits.

"

How to handle stress? Drink coffee and eat tons
of chocolate . . . just kidding . . . kind of. Just stay even
keel and calm and take one task at a time. Multitasking is
great, but if it is going to turn you into a stress-ball that
particular day, then one task at a time is a better choice. I
try to think to myself that stressing out or getting worked
up is not going to help anything or anyone, so why do it?

MELODY QUAMMEN, CVT
Montrose, Colorado

Our jobs are full of difficult days; it comes with the territory. Often we are juggling many things. Even the term *multitasking* can be deceptive, because though you are balancing many needs or requests at one time, you can give your full attention to only one thing at a time. It's important to recognize that and actually give your *full* attention to each task. This is the only way to be sure you do each task correctly and to the best of your ability, rather than giving only 75 percent of your effort because you're so concerned about the next things on your list. Melody is right: getting stressed-out doesn't help you do a better job, on any level. So take a deep breath, then dive in!

"

Euthanasia is never easy. Since I have dealt with that situation many times with my own pets, it just comes natural to understand what a client is going through and stay strong for his or her sake. Still now after ten years in this field, especially with a client and patient I knew well, sometimes I cannot help sobbing . . . and that is okay, too. Explaining to clients that euthanasia is the most humane gift they can give their pets to get rid of their pain and suffering is helpful.

Lyndi M. Watson, LVT
Tampa, Florida

"

Other medical professions deal with death, but it is estimated that veterinary medicine deals with death or the topic of death five to eight times more. Veterinary medicine is really the only profession that administers a peaceful passing to relieve suffering in our patients. As difficult as this can be for the family, we take comfort in the fact that the patient is no longer suffering. We often provide our clients with tools to help them cope with the grief, but how often do we look inside ourselves to gauge how it is affecting us? Whether your practice sees death or euthanasia only occasionally or sees it every day, you need to recognize what it means to each person on the team. Even just talking about it after the fact is a sign that we are dealing with the feelings and trying to help each other cope. Your practice can implement a "critical incident debriefing" policy whereby, after a crisis or particularly stressful event, there is a brief but important conversation about the event and recognition of how it affected members of the team. (Some may feel inclined to seek additional help from a friend, the manager, or an outside professional if they know that it's okay to address the feelings our difficult jobs bring us daily.) Stop, take a moment to identify how you feel, and see if you're okay before moving on. Then demonstrate that you care for the others on your team who are walking in the same shoes by extending them a shoulder to cry on or a helping hand.

To relieve stress, I sing silly songs I make up. I will get on the intercom and sing a ditty that it's time to gather for morning rounds. We play music in the treatment area (not too loud). We have theme potluck lunches, like Soup Day. Everyone brings a favorite recipe, and we all share. We celebrate each other's birthdays by signing up to make cakes for one another. We try to have fun and laugh often.

SUZANNE WICKHAM, RVT
Youngsville, North Carolina

The next best thing to humor is music. Songs with an uplifting beat, at a lower volume of course, can really help sustain a positive outlook among team members. You may get a song stuck in your head, but that's better than some of the thoughts that might linger there during a bad day. Sharing the fun, such as potlucks or team celebrations, is also a good idea. Coming together to do our best work *and* enjoy life to the fullest is a great way to solidify the team.

The best advice I ever got as a veterinary
technician was short and sweet:
"You've been here fourteen hours, go home!"

ELISE M. ATKINSON, BA, CVT
Lakewood, Colorado

L ong days, grueling nights, double shifts, being short-staffed . . . we've been through the ringer and then some during our days in veterinary practice. Yet we come back, day after day, to heal the pets and help the people who make this a wonderful profession to be in.

Clear expectations, written directions, and open lines of verbal communication are all important. None of us took mind reading in school, and this particular skill should not be expected on a regular basis. We can do this periodically, just to keep them on their toes!

ANN WORTINGER, BIS, LVT, VTS (ECC, SAIM)
Detroit, Michigan

It is true: mind reading is not a prerequisite or a required course in veterinary schools or veterinary technology programs! It might be helpful if we had this capacity, but it's probably best that we don't know the inner workings of every mind around us. Therefore we need expectations that are clearly defined, protocols that are written and documented, and verbal communication that serves to strengthen the practice. If you can happen to read the mind of your veterinarian or coworker occasionally, it might at least let you catch someone off balance from time to time . . . all in good fun, of course.

By doing the best possible job that I can through
attention to detail and continuing education,
I can earn the respect of the team. When I
strive for excellence, veterinarians are more
likely to respect me and the profession.

MINDY BOUGH, CVT
Urbana, Illinois

As a veterinary technician dedicated to continual learning, you are positively representing the profession to the veterinarians and the entire team. Continuing education isn't only for technicians, and it's important to be a positive role model for all positions. Yet it isn't enough to just attend continuing education courses. Your absence from the practice isn't what gains you respect; it is coming back and teaching others. It's easy to see where technical skills or medical information can be beneficial for the medical team, but it takes more creativity to decipher how these topics may affect the front office team. For example, the technicians will be interested in learning how to place a new type of catheter; the front office staff will appreciate knowing enough about the new catheter to explain to a client the different type of charge on an invoice. Although veterinarians are the leaders of the medical team, they will also be impressed with your newfound knowledge and skills.

"

I try to make each employee feel that he or she is important, and his or her voice counts. It is important to listen to all staff members, and respond in a level, goal-oriented manner. No question or comment is unimportant, and everyone needs to feel needed and respected. If everyone on staff feels this way, then the clinic runs smoothly as a team, creating efficiency, and ultimately improving capabilities and income.

MAXINE T. HLADKY, LVT
Henderson, Nevada

"

Long gone are the days of authoritarian management, when the manager said "Jump!" and the employee responded, "How high?" Now a successful manager will explain why it's important to jump, determine if the employee is capable of jumping and has received adequate training on the jump process, and then hold a staff meeting to get a consensus on just how high is "high" in the opinions of the group! Now more than ever, every single team member must feel important and respected for his or her opinion. There should be give-and-take of questions and answers, inquiries and explanations. The best practices are managed by those who know how to inspire the best performance from their team, while delivering appropriate praise and rewards for a job well done.

I find that clients are willing to talk about their pet, and usually come up with funny or fascinating stories. They also usually tell you about how they acquired their pet. Being a technician is not only dealing with animals, but also being a good listener to clients and their concerns.

PAMELA S. MOROSKY, RVT
Minerva, Ohio

Pet parents are proud, and many carry pictures of their pets with them. They would love to show them to you! You can also strengthen your bond with pet families by expressing interest in hearing the stories that they would love to tell you about their furry family members. Sometimes there may be no one else in their lives who can appreciate the bond they share with their pets, so your role becomes even more important. Clients choose our practice not only because of the medical care we provide, but also for the personal care we deliver to both them and their pets. A technician will secure his or her place in the practice by being technically proficient and fluent in speaking the language of pet lovers.

Continuing education is the cornerstone
of our profession; I make time.

ALISON GOTTLIEB, BS, RVT, VTS (ECC)
Cedar Grove, New Jersey

Veterinary medicine will continue to change, and we must remain on the cutting edge to provide the best medicine to our patients and best information to our clients. With so many options for acquiring continuing education—conferences, seminars, meetings, journals, online courses, listservs, associations, societies, etc.—there is no reason not to stay current on the technology that enhances veterinary medicine and makes it possible to provide the best patient care.

A front office team member is not "just a receptionist," and hopefully he or she never feels this way. The front office team is the front line, the people the client first talks to and forms an impression of about the practice. They set the tone of the practice, especially when dealing with emergencies or crisis with a family's pet. They are key to the flow of the practice and should be valued and appreciated for everything they do. It definitely takes the right person, and it is very gratifying to hear clients say "thank you" and know they really mean it!

Tania Hmurovich, CVA

Each individual on the team is important, and Tania has a wonderful way of explaining just how important the members of the front office team are to the practice of veterinary medicine. They are important ambassadors for our practices and for the profession, as they are the first level of contact with the general public. Yet sometimes even our own practices do not lead the way in achieving mutual respect between the front office team and the rest of the staff. Too often front office team members feel they are "just receptionists," and have even been known to utter those words when asked a question they cannot answer. This is a shame, and all of us are to blame. Practice leaders must strive to include front office team members in practice decisions and create mutual respect within the team. Most important, they must ensure that front office team members believe in themselves and the importance of their position on the front lines.

As a technician I am the liaison between the doctors
and the client. I make them feel more comfortable
and am able to spend more time with them explaining
procedures and diagnostics. We provide the more caring
aspect of the work instead of just the diagnostic aspect.

SUSAN EVANS, CVT
Wilton, Connecticut

Susan clearly recognizes the important role veterinary technicians play in client service. We are often able to devote more time to explaining services and care, answering questions, and putting clients at ease. It is important for clients to trust the support team of the veterinary practice, and allowing this time for interaction helps to cement the bond of the family with the practice. Just as important as a correct diagnosis is the family's perception of the care given.

All small things done well equal one great big thing. If there is not full participation by one small part, the big thing isn't as big and great.

JESSICA MCDONALD, LVT, VTS (ECC), PRACTICE MANAGER
St. Cloud, Minnesota

Each person on the team is important to reaching the goals of patient care and client service. Every step of the way depends on someone, and the combined efforts of individuals will help to reach the goal. From the first contact with the client at the front desk, through his or her experience in the exam room, and to exit from the practice, the client's satisfaction depends on a variety of people doing their jobs the best way possible. This is how many small things equal one great client experience. In the process of providing excellent patient care, it is important for the front office team to schedule the visit correctly, for the assistant to ask the right questions upon drop-off, and for the technician to carry out the orders of the attending veterinarian. All these steps culminate in the best patient care. The chain is made stronger when there are no weak links.

Find something you are passionate about and pursue that area of interest. Your enthusiasm will become contagious, and your coworkers will soon associate you with your passion and you will be the expert or go-to gal.

DAWN BOLKA, BSBA, RVT
Michigan City, Indiana

It is helpful to know before a job interview where your interests lie, so you can inquire whether that role exists or is already filled in that particular practice. Perhaps you really enjoy performing lab work, but they already have a full-time laboratory technician. Is there something else you want to do, or do you need to look elsewhere for an opportunity? If client education is your passion, that can likely be done by more than one person in the practice, so you could be a great fit for that team. As Dawn points out, as you assume the role you want most, your enthusiasm will show, and others will turn to you when they need your specific skill or knowledge.

The best way to encourage others to believe in
the mission of the practice is to believe and follow
it yourself every day and every moment. If you
want people to smile, smile at them, thank them,
acknowledge a day's work with a thank-you.

VIRGINIA JONES
Monroe, Washington

You may be able to look around at the team and identify those you feel are not exemplifying the mission of the practice, but have you looked in the mirror and made sure that you are a good role model for others? It's often easier to see the failings of others than to realize how much better we can be ourselves. The mission is more than words; it is a way of life while you are at work. If you help to model this mission, others will follow. If you model a positive attitude and kind disposition, others will do the same. After all, smiles are contagious. And it isn't just your mother who will be proud of you using "please" and "thank you" on a regular basis.

The veterinarians at my practice don't always utilize me to my fullest. I have to remind them that they have other (often I use the words "more important") things to do with their time. Sometimes I just start helping them or take over the task.

CHRISTINA CHATHAM

It is often true that the veterinarian will have "more important" things to do; just as often, the technician or assistant is simply more qualified or experienced to handle the task. Veterinarians were taught how to be doctors, veterinary technicians are skilled in the nursing and care of patients, and assistants care about the comfort of patients. Yet because that veterinarian is primarily responsible for the outcome of patient care, he or she is justifiably cautious and wants to oversee the process. Once the veterinarian is certain that the team can provide patient care at the desired level, he or she will easily move on to more "doctor duties" and leave the patients in the care of the support team.

To encourage continuous learning, we have open
communication between the doctors and staff.
The doctors are always willing to share their knowledge
and teach employees new things. Also, it's important
to read veterinary publications and visit veterinary
websites and take webinars. Learning never ends; you
just need to take advantage of it when it presents itself.

Dana M. Grab, CVT
Willingboro, New Jersey

R emain open to learning. The Veterinary Technician Oath reflects this commitment: "I accept my obligations to . . . further my knowledge and competence through a commitment to lifelong learning." When you attend continuing education events, you must expect to take something away with you at the end. Open yourself up to that expectation and allow yourself to be taught. Before you attend a CE event, take a few moments to think about the topic and why you are attending. Write down several things you want to learn, and make sure you write down the corresponding answers as they are given or ask questions of the instructor or speaker so you are sure to get the information you want and need. There is also a lot to learn on a daily basis. Either during or at the end of your shift each day, take a moment to write down one new thing you learned that day. You learn something new every day, if you can only pause to acknowledge it.

You must break down the time in levels of importance.
I do it in four levels: burning, need to do, can wait, and
can be dropped. I then take the hardest first and work
my way to the more simple tasks. I always delegate what
can be to a responsible person on my team. Be sure to
pay attention to what is important to the practice owner!

STEPHEN TRACEY, HOSPITAL MANAGER
Princeton, New Jersey

S tephen describes a wonderful way to organize your "to do" list. When we can realize that not everything has the same urgency, we can prioritize our lists much more easily. A good resource on this type of organizational scheme is *Getting Things Done* by David Allen (Penguin, 2001). However, it is often difficult to jump into the most difficult work first; we tend to want to knock out some of the more simple duties first so we can feel that measure of accomplishment that comes from crossing things off our list! It is imperative to know what is most important to the practice owner. Sometimes this is easy; sometimes it is more difficult. It helps if you can keep a running list of projects that are pending, in stages of completion, and completed. Then, at regular intervals, discuss your project list with your manager or practice owner. Let that person help you prioritize your lengthy list, and be sure you're on track with what really should be considered "burning."

To enhance communication between the front
and back, have the medical staff run the front
office for an afternoon on a Monday!

SARAH ELLIOTT, BA/EDUCATION, CVT
Osage, Iowa

Here's one solution that just might open some eyes, although the front office staff will probably be reluctant to turn over their territory to the technicians for the day, and the technicians would probably give up the opportunity to switch! The interesting thing is that although technicians often will admit to not wanting to work up front because it is a difficult job dealing with clients all day long, they do not transfer that opinion into a healthy respect for those who do the job up front. It is said that walking a mile in someone else's shoes will change your life . . . or at least you may stub your toe!

Making work fun comes from teamwork
and respect for your coworkers. If you love
what you do, you always have fun.

DEBBIE POINDEXTER, RVT, AND
BROOK KLEIN, VETERINARY ASSISTANT
Cumming, Georgia

A team that has fun together often has laid a foundation of cooperation and mutual respect. This allows them to look past their differences and find humor in their individual and shared experiences. Most important, you must love what you do. You must continue to be inspired and remain open to the calling that brought you to this profession.

When I feel burned out, I rely on my faith to help
me keep perspective. I enjoy crafts and reading, and
I get lots of "purr" therapy from my cats. Sometimes
you just need that unconditional love from a
beloved pet at the end of a long day. It also helps
to talk about burnout and the fact that it exists.

SUZANNE WICKHAM, RVT
Youngsville, North Carolina

A bsolutely, talk about burnout *and* compassion fatigue. Burnout may be minimized by talking with the team and figuring out ways to even out the workload or rejuvenate the team after a hectic shift. Compassion fatigue is minimized by opening up the conversation and first and foremost acknowledging that it exists. It is important that we take care of ourselves, but we can also teach others how to help the team in general. There is a concept called "low-impact disclosure." Instead of taking a hard shift, difficult client, or traumatic patient experience and dumping the details on our coworkers, we should ask their permission to help us carry that load and let them keep control of how much detail we dump on them. We all know that laughter is contagious; so is stress, in the most basic sense. You certainly don't need to bring everyone down just to feel less alone; rather, let your colleagues help pull you up. Then give yourself some "purr therapy"! Suzanne makes another good point: it is important to have hobbies outside of veterinary medicine to engage our time and spirits. Even though you are very busy with your career, you have to create some free time for yourself and fill it with meaning. This may be difficult to do, because you may have forgotten what your hobbies are while you have been so busy! So pretend you have a whole week off with absolutely nothing to do—no work, no chores, no kids to taxi around, no spouse to clean up after—just you and a quiet house. What would you do to fill your time? What activities would you enjoy indulging in? Where would you go, and what would you do there? Now take a few of those activities and work them into your life, at least once a week. Put aside "me time" to balance your life.

It's one thing to tell doctors that I can do the job, but it's quite another to actually follow through. So I not only volunteer to do a specific task but I perform the task diligently and expertly to the best of my ability. Then and only then do the doctors trust me again in the future.

DAVID M. LAWRENCE, CVT

Trust, like respect, is earned, and the best way to earn a veterinarian's trust is to demonstrate what you can do and do it to the best of your ability. Prove what you can contribute, even if you must take baby steps, and you will be asked to continue and enhance that contribution. Once you prove yourself, the veterinarian will give you more opportunities to shine in the future.

My advice is, try *everything*! Ask the technician you are working with everything you can, and touch the equipment. See what it feels like to perform these tasks; try to rotate through every area for one week or one month. If you think you like something, stay away for a month and come back to it. Your heart will be excited when you find the perfect spot.

Krystal Sobrino, AAS, LVT, CVT, Hospital Manager
Scottsdale, Arizona

Cross-training, job rotation, or job swapping is good for the practice, and it's also good for the person! You can try on different hats, and see which one fits best or which one complements your skills and talents best. If job rotation is not already part of the staff experience, approach management or your supervisor about what you want to do. At the very least, you can help fill voids when others take vacations or the practice experiences unexpected absences. Try a new position for a short time to see if it stimulates a deeper interest within you. When your heart is happy, it will be reflected in the work you do and positively influence the team around you.

Time: what is that, when you work sixty hours a
week? I make sure that I go to at least one conference
a year and actually attend a few full days of lectures.
I also keep journals near my bed and try to read
an article before bed once or twice a week.

Alexandra Dashkevicz, BS, BA, CVT
Manalapan, New Jersey

Time can be elusive, yet a commitment to our profession requires that we devote time to our trade. Attending a conference is an important way to stay motivated and network with others. We also need to find spare moments to read a short article.

You'll discover your place in the practice by participating in all areas of the hospital and not being afraid or intimidated by new, unfamiliar things. It's hard to know if you have a hidden talent or will enjoy something without giving it a chance.

CASANDRA FERRELL, AAS, CVT
Denver, Colorado

What if you're not quite sure what role you want to assume in the practice, or perhaps you are ready to consider a change? Then try all sorts of new things, as Casandra mentions, and see what tickles your fancy. Ask questions and be observant of others' roles in the practice. Be prepared for your career to take many twists and turns, and enjoy the ride!

Remember to get your puppy kisses and
kitten cuddles while you can so they can
help you get through the rough times.

CHRISTINA MULLINS, RVT
Loveland, Ohio

I t's important always to focus on the reason we are here: those puppies, kittens, and other pets that enrich our lives and the lives of our clients. Despite the rough times, there is nothing better than puppy breath and kitten mews. Have you had your share of cuddles this week?

REFERENCES

Allen, David. 2001. *Getting Things Done: The Art of Stress-Free Productivity.* Penguin.

Cameron, Julia. 2007. *The Complete Artist's Way: Creativity as a Spiritual Practice.* Penguin.

Figley, Charles R., and Robert G. Roop. 2006. *Compassion Fatigue in the Animal-Care Community.* Humane Society Press.

Maslach, C. 1982. "Understanding burnout: Definitional issues in analyzing a complex phenomenon," in *Job stress and burnout: Research, theory and intervention perspectives,* ed. W.S. Paine. Sage Publication.

McCurnin, Dennis M., and Joanna M. Bassert. 2006. *Clinical Textbook for Veterinary Technicians,* 6th ed. Elsevier/Saunders.

Nakaya, Shannon Fujimoto, DVM. 2005. *Kindred Spirit, Kindred Care: Making Health Decisions on Behalf of Our Animal Companions.* New World Library.

Rose, Rebecca, CVT, and Carin Smith, DVM. 2009. *Career Choices for Veterinary Technicians.* AAHA Press.

Wolfelt, Alan D., PhD. 2004. *When Your Pet Dies: A Guide to Mourning, Remembering, and Healing.* Companion Press.

ABOUT THE AUTHOR

Katherine Dobbs, RVT, CVPM, PHR, began her career in veterinary medicine as a registered veterinary technician in 1992. Since that time, her love of animals and the veterinary profession has led her toward practice management and human resources. She has moved into a career of consulting with the intention of helping all veterinary professionals discover or maintain a career path that is both personally satisfying and professionally successful. Recently Katherine has become a compassion fatigue specialist, writing and speaking frequently on this topic at conferences and private practices. She is a member of VetPartners, where she sits on two task forces, for human resources and specialty practice issues. Katherine has been published in *AAHA Trends*, *Firstline*, *Veterinary Economics*, *Veterinary Practice News*, and *Veterinary Technician Journal* (she is a member of the *VTJ* editorial board and has been the featured author of the "Management Matters" column). She teaches online for VSPN, focusing on compassion fatigue courses and a CVPM preparatory review course, as well as various courses for the referral practice team. Her public speaking experience includes the TNAVC, WVC, AAHA, AVMA, IVECCS, VSIPP, and many state veterinary medical association and technician conferences.